SAN DIEGO ZOO
PANDA TREK

BECKON BOOKS

WORLD TRAVELER
Su Lin, pictured as a cub in San Diego, was born at the Zoo in 2005. She left the Zoo in August 2010 and moved to the mountains of Sichuan Province, China.

A Trek Through China

The San Diego Zoo's Panda Trek journeys into the mountainous bamboo forests of southwest China, home to the critically endangered giant panda. With a stone portal marking the entrance, the exhibit is designed to evoke a visit to China's Wolong Nature Reserve. There, Zoo researchers have partnered with Chinese scientists since 1996 to learn more about the giant panda.

The exhibit begins with a replica of a rustic research hut, which contains panda tracking collars, a radio-signal receiver, and reference books. In the wild, scientists use huts like this as a base camp in their search for the elusive giant panda. It can take days or weeks of diligent scouting through the densely clouded, high-elevation forests—often through torrential rainstorms—to catch just one glimpse! At Panda Trek, visitors can also look for evidence of giant pandas. These clues include a pale green pile of realistic panda scat, paw prints on the ground, and scratches or scent markings on a tree.

Along the way, visitors will see other animals that share the giant pandas' forest habitat: rare rock-climbing Sichuan takins, raccoon-like red pandas, and Mang Mountain vipers. Finally, beyond a bridge that crosses a mountain stream, are two of the four giant pandas on research loan from the People's Republic of China. As the ancient Chinese proverb says, "The journey is the reward."

RUSTIC QUARTERS
This replica hut displays some of the tools and books that researchers use when studying elusive giant pandas, their habitat, and the other wildlife that live there.

MILESTONE MOMENTS

China's oldest known poem, which mentions the giant panda, was written 3,000 years ago. But it wasn't until March 11, 1869, that the first Westerner, French missionary and amateur naturalist Père Armand David, wrote about the "fine skin of the famous black and white bear" shot by hunters in Ya'an, Sichuan Province.

JUST LIKE HOME
Panda Trek is designed to evoke the Wolong Nature Reserve, nestled high in the mountains of western China. The Chinese characters on the left of the entrance say "Bai Yun"; the ones on the right say "Gao Gao."

THE NAME GAME
Red pandas were discovered by Western scientists before giant pandas. The word *panda* is thought to originate from Nepalese words that mean "bamboo-footed."

Takin Terrain

The Sichuan takin—pronounced "ta-kin"—has two sharp horns like a wildebeest, a nose like a moose, a tail like a bear, and a large, stocky body like a bison. Adults weigh between 550 and 880 pounds. Despite their hefty size, takins can jump like an antelope six feet in the air from a standing start and leap nimbly from rock to rock.

Takins have some remarkable adaptations to help them survive the bitter cold of winter in the Himalayan Mountains. A thick oil coating on their shaggy fur works like a rain slicker in wet weather, and during the winter, they grow a second, shorter undercoat. Takins also have large nasal passages that warm incoming air and help preserve their body heat.

Herd size varies with the seasons. In spring and summer, as many as 300 takins gather at altitudes of 11,000 feet to feed on the leaves and bark of alpine and deciduous trees and shrubs. In the fall and winter, they separate into smaller groups of 10 to 35 animals and migrate to the forested valleys at 4,000 feet. Takins use the same routes over and over, creating well-worn paths through the dense thickets of bamboo and rhododendrons.

BABY STEPS
Within a couple of days of birth, a takin kid can follow its mother through most types of terrain. If a kid somehow becomes separated from its mother during the first few months, it gives a panicked noise that sounds like a lion cub.

NATIONAL TREASURES
Takins, like giant pandas, are considered national treasures in China.

With their powerful bodies and impressive horns, these "goat antelopes" have few natural enemies in the wild. Like the giant pandas, however, takins are endangered due to loss of habitat through human activities such as farming, mining, and logging. They are also vulnerable to climate change. The government of China has given takins full protection under the law and has set aside two reserves for their protection.

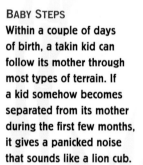

MILESTONE MOMENTS

In 1989, the San Diego Zoo became the first zoo in the Western Hemisphere to successfully breed takins outside of China. Since then, there have been more than 50 Sichuan takins born here!

MOUNTAIN CLIMBERS
Takins at the San Diego Zoo have been known to jump six-foot walls from a standing start!

BUFFET BROWSERS
Takins eat almost every kind of vegetation. If the leaves are out of reach, they use their powerful bodies to push over small trees to bring those leaves closer.

"The takins know their names and are clever at getting attention. If we're working in the back area and Lian, our adult male, is there, he puts his front legs on the top stall bar so that he's standing upright. In that position, he's 10 feet tall! We know he's just looking for attention, because he just stands there quietly waiting for us to tell him to get down."

— Kathy Hawk, *senior keeper*

TRUE COLORS
While the majority of a Mang Mountain pit viper's body is green and brown, the tail end is light blue. This adaptation is used to lure prey.

Mang Mountain Pit Viper

I n southern China, Mang Mountain National Park lays coiled near the Changping District like a giant snake. Nestled into the forests of this region are deadly Mang Mountain pit vipers. Reaching lengths of up to seven feet, these snakes have mottled gray and green skin that camouflages them against moss-covered logs and rocks while they wait to ambush rodents or other small prey. Like other pit vipers, Mang Mountain

vipers have a pit between their eyes and nostrils. The opening leads to a special organ that helps them to sense body heat from other animals and judge where to strike.

Mang Mountain pit vipers hibernate in deep underground dens during the winter. These elusive snakes were little known outside of China and were not classified by scientists until the early 1990s. The San Diego Zoo is one of only a few places in the world to successfully care for them.

FEEL THE HEAT
All pit vipers have tiny depressions of infrared-sensitive tissue between their eyes and nostrils, which allow them to sense the body heat of potential prey or predators.

POISON CONTROL
Vipers can control—and therefore, conserve—their venom secretion. They can release venom through the left fang, the right fang, both fangs at once, or none at all.

The Other (Red) Panda

Red pandas may share the same habitat, diet, and part of the same name as giant pandas, but that's where the similarities end. While giant pandas belong to the bear family, red pandas are linked to raccoons. In fact, these small, beautiful mammals have been classified as a species all their own: *Ailurus fulgens*, which means "fire-colored cat," a nod to their catlike features and striking coloring.

Red pandas spend most of their time in the canopy of old growth trees. With semi-retractable claws for climbing and a long ringed tail for balance, they're tree dwellers for a reason. Tree climbing gives these pint-sized pandas access to the tender tops and young leaves of nearby bamboo stalks, their main source of food.

PANDA PAIRS
In the wild, red pandas are solitary except during breeding season, which occurs from January to April.

To process bamboo, a low-energy food, red pandas have developed an extraordinarily low metabolism (much like a sloth). This causes them to sleep most of the day, feeding at dawn and dusk. They also reproduce only during warm weather, when food is most plentiful. Female red pandas are fertile for just one or two days a year. Their gestation period, 135 days, is long for animals of their size, and their cubs mature relatively slowly—between 12 and 18 months.

IN THE FIELD

Red pandas are endangered: It is estimated that just 2,500 live in the wild. Their habitat—which consists of old growth forests in China—has been threatened in recent years by logging and farming. Red pandas are also threatened by the pet trade. The San Diego Zoo supports the Red Panda Network, a community-based conservation program in Nepal that hires local forest guardians to maintain camera traps in the forest, talk to local people, and give educational presentations about the importance of preserving the red panda.

RED, WHITE, AND CAMOUFLAGED
With their reddish coat and white face, red pandas blend in easily among the red moss and white lichen that cover the tree trunks and branches of their forest homes.

MILESTONE MOMENTS

The red panda was "discovered" in China by British and French naturalists in 1821. For nearly 50 years, it was the only panda known to the Western world. Westerners renamed the smaller red panda "the lesser panda" in 1869 after the giant panda was introduced to the Western world. That term is no longer used for this one-of-a-kind animal.

TREE HUGGER
Gao Gao, who has fathered numerous cubs with Bai Yun, does not climb high trees very often. Most of the time, he prefers to lean against them while eating bamboo.

All About Giant Pandas

Giant pandas are a national treasure in China and protected by law. Affectionately called "large bear cats" by the Chinese, giant pandas been portrayed in Chinese art dating back thousands of years. The rest of the world didn't discover these beloved bears, however, until French missionary Pére Armand David first described them in 1869.

Like other bears, giant pandas are stocky, have a pigeon-toed walk, and are good climbers. But they're unique in many ways: While they have unusually heavy bones for their size, giant pandas are very flexible. (They like to do somersaults!) Even though their diet is 99 percent bamboo, they are technically carnivores. And of course, they have distinctive black-and-white markings that develop shortly after they are born.

Giant pandas inhabit a home range of up to 100 square miles. They spend most of their time eating and sleeping, leaving their territory only when they're searching for new food supplies or a mate. Unfortunately, their natural habitat is shrinking due to deforestation and encroaching development. An estimated 1,600 remain in their habitat, with another 300 in zoos. Worldwide collaborative efforts—including breeding programs, panda reserves, and research initiatives—are in place to help conserve these rare creatures.

BEST FACE FORWARD
Bai Yun, the Zoo's matriarch, has given birth to six cubs since her arrival in San Diego in 1996.

BEAR HUGS
Born in August 2009, Yun Zi plays with his mom, Bai Yun. As panda cubs mature, the Zoo begins to train them by reinforcing certain behaviors to help with their veterinary care.

Did You Know?

Unlike other bears that live in cold areas, giant pandas don't hibernate during the winter. They do not store up fat like other bears, so they migrate to lower, warmer elevations where they can continue to feed.

JUST FOR KICKS
Hua Mei was born at the San Diego Zoo via in vitro fertilization in 1999. She was the first giant panda born in the United States to survive to adulthood.

SNOW FUN
Bai Yun and her cub Hua Mei enjoy one of the Zoo's special snow days. The temperature and texture of the machine-made snow are a sensory treat!

MILESTONE MOMENTS

Between 1957 and 1983, the government of China bequeathed 24 pandas to other countries as diplomatic gifts. This included the 1972 gift of Ling-Ling and Hsing-Hsing to First Lady Pat Nixon following President Richard Nixon's historic visit to China. Mrs. Nixon donated the pandas to the National Zoo in Washington, D.C.

"Gao Gao has never been much of a tree climber, preferring to stay on the ground. What he loves to do is eat! He reminds me of a guy on a permanent vacation; he doesn't want to have to go too far or work too hard for his food. Yet he has a playful side, too. He loves a tub filled with scented wood shavings—it's party time!"

— Kathy Hawk, *senior keeper*

THROUGH THE TREES
Like his brothers and sisters before him, Yun Zi
is an avid tree climber. But he has a style all
his own—a rough-and-tumble approach that
required Zoo staff to replace a tree in his yard
with one that could stand up to Yun Zi's antics.

Who's Been at the Zoo?

Since 1987, the San Diego Zoo has been privileged to care for a number of giant pandas, each with their own unique personality. All of the pandas have arrived as part of a special agreement with the Chinese government. Under this agreement, any cubs born to the pandas must be sent to China after their third birthday. Over the years, Zoo staff and visitors have bid farewell to four giant panda cubs and one adult male, who retired to his country of birth. These pandas, however, will always be part of the Zoo's family.

MELLOW FELLOW
Shi Shi arrived with Bai Yun in 1996. An older panda, he preferred following a routine of resting, eating, and sleeping.

Did You Know?

Giant pandas have lived in China's bamboo forests for several million years.

MEAL TIME
Cubs like Zhen Zhen begin to experiment with eating bamboo at around four months old. They mimic their mothers as they practice grasping, biting, and chewing the leaves.

MOTHER-DAUGHTER BOND
Hua Mei and her mom, Bai Yun, made their public debut in the Zoo's exhibit area when Hua Mei was six months old.

Bai Yun ("White Cloud"), Female

Born: September 7, 1991, Wolong Giant Panda Reserve, Sichuan Province, China
At the San Diego Zoo: Since September 1996

Bai Yun was the first successful birth among the pandas in China's Wolong Giant Panda Reserve in Sichuan Province. She arrived in San Diego just days after her fifth birthday. Curious, unpredictable, and mischievous, she has earned the name of "Teflon bear," because no amount of rain, dirt, or mud seems to stick to her bright white coat. Bai Yun was frisky and friendly with her first mate, 20-year-old Shi Shi, and can be downright flirtatious with her second and current mate, Gao Gao. Bai Yun has given birth to six cubs (so far) and has proven to be an excellent mother.

"Bai Yun has always been great at figuring out how to get food out of the puzzle feeders. We make different kinds and try to make some extra challenging, but Bai Yun sticks with it until she conquers it, while Gao Gao will give up pretty quickly."

— Kathy Hawk, *senior keeper*

Shi Shi ("Rock"), Male

**Born: Mid-1970s, in the wild in China's
Sichuan Province
At the San Diego Zoo: September 1996 to January 2003
Died: July 5, 2008, Guangzhou Zoo**

In March 1992, Shi Shi was found critically wounded—probably from a fight with another male panda—and taken to the Wolong Giant Panda Reserve. Because of his injuries, he could not be returned to his native habitat. He came to San Diego as part of a research loan in September 1996. Significantly older than female Bai Yun (and not especially interested in mating), Shi Shi fathered Bai Yun's first cub, Hua Mei, through artificial insemination. He returned to China in 2003 and lived out his retirement in the Guangzhou Zoo.

Hua Mei ("China USA"), Female

Born: August 21, 1999, San Diego Zoo
At the San Diego Zoo: August 1999 to February 2004
Current Home: Wolong Giant Panda Reserve, Sichuan Province, China

Hua Mei's birth to Bai Yun via artificial insemination was historic. Millions of people followed Hua Mei as she grew up, confident and always curious. In 2004, per the Zoo's research agreement with China, Hua Mei returned to her mother's birthplace, the Wolong Giant Panda Reserve in Sichuan Province. Since then, Hua Mei has made history a second time by giving birth to three sets of twins and three single cubs. Wolong researchers named her a "heroic mother" after she gave birth to her seventh cub.

Gao Gao ("High High" or "Tall Tall"), Male

**Born: Estimated 1990, in the wild near China's Fengtongzhai Giant Panda Reserve
At the San Diego Zoo: Since January 2003**

Gao Gao (pronounced "Gow Gow") had a difficult beginning. Still a cub in March 1993, he was found in the wild, injured and dehydrated, with the left side of his head bloodied from losing two thirds of his ear. Researchers at China's Fengtongzhai Giant Panda Reserve nursed him back to health, and in 1994, they released him back into the wild. In 2002, however, Gao Gao was brought to the Wolong Reserve after he was deemed too disruptive to local villages. He arrived in San Diego in January 2003, rambunctious, inquisitive, alert, and always hungry. (Keepers call him a bamboo-eating machine!) Famous for his handstands, he's also passed along an uncommon genetic trait—webbed back toes—to four of the five cubs he has sired with Bai Yun.

> *"Every so often, Gao Gao will turn his back to the fence, which is his way of asking the keepers for a back scratch. He really gets into it, pawing his ears and rolling on the ground with pleasure."*
>
> — Kathy Hawk, *senior keeper*

Mei Sheng ("Born in the USA" or "Beautiful Life"), Male

Born: August 19, 2003, San Diego Zoo
At the San Diego Zoo: August 2003 to November 2007
Current Home: Bifengxia Giant Panda Reserve, Sichuan Province, China

Mei Sheng was the second cub born at the San Diego Zoo, the first from the pairing of Bai Yun and Gao Gao. A sweet and playful cub, he was also reserved, sensitive, and cautious, never roaming far from the security of his mother. In 2007, Mei Sheng returned to his mother's home base, the Wolong Giant Panda Reserve. In February 2008, Mei Sheng was transferred to the Bifengxia Reserve. The following year, Bifengxia researchers reported his first successful mating.

"While we get attached to every bear that has ever called the Giant Panda Research Station home, we always try to focus on our primary goal: giant panda conservation. All of our efforts, from research to husbandry and education, are designed to enhance our knowledge of these incredible bears so we can ensure they have a future in the wild."

— Megan Owen, *conservation program manager*

Su Lin ("A Little Bit of Something Very Cute"), Female

Born: August 2, 2005, San Diego Zoo
At the San Diego Zoo: August 2005 to September 2010
Current Home: Bifengxia Giant Panda Reserve, Sichuan Province, China

In Chinese, the number three is similar to the character for "birth" and is considered lucky. Bai Yun's third cub, Su Lin, was a shy, sensitive youngster who wouldn't disturb her mother's nap, even at feeding time. She was known for her acrobatic sleeping positions on the highest branches of the trees. Su Lin also liked to rearrange things in her exhibit, earning the staff's nickname "the redecorating diva." She was sent to China in 2010, where she bred successfully with a wild-born male and gave birth to a male cub on July 7, 2011.

Zhen Zhen ("Precious"), Female

Born: August 3, 2007, San Diego Zoo
At the San Diego Zoo: August 2007 to September 2010
Current Home: Bifengxia Giant Panda Reserve, Sichuan Province, China

Bai Yun's fourth cub, her third with Gao Gao, received her name in a special way—through an online naming poll among San Diego Zoo panda fans. After narrowing the field from 2,400 names to four finalists, Zhen Zhen (pronounced "Jun Jun") was the favorite. A fast learner and high achiever, Zhen Zhen charmed Zoo visitors with her playful antics and amazed keepers with her deft problem-solving skills. She left with her big sister Su Lin for Sichuan Province in September 2010.

Yun Zi ("Son of Cloud"), Male

Born: August 5, 2009, San Diego Zoo
At the San Diego Zoo: Since August 2009

On the day Yun Zi was born—Bai Yun's fifth cub, her fourth sired by Gao Gao—the San Diego Zoo's popular Panda Cam website crashed under the demand of worldwide onlookers and well wishers. The little guy was shy at first, preferring the peace and quiet of his mother's den to his more public play yard. Gradually, however, he gained confidence, energy, and speed, turning into a romping, belly-flopping, branch-ripping, scent-marking dervish. When keepers realized he was systematically deconstructing the large climbing/sleeping tree that had withstood the antics of all four of his older siblings, they made plans for a bigger, more permanent tree that will hopefully survive Yun Zi's adolescence.

"Sometimes it seems Yun Zi has his own idea of what his habitat should look like. We lovingly call him 'Mr. Destructo.' He likes to dash up and down the climbing structures, throwing bamboo, breaking branches off trees, then dragging them to a different spot. It's one of his favorite things to do!"

— Jennifer Becerra, *senior keeper*

A Bamboo Buffet

Giant pandas spend at least 12 hours a day eating bamboo. Because bamboo is so low in nutrients, they need to eat a lot of it—about half their body weight each day! There are about 25 edible varieties of bamboo in China. Since bamboo dies after it blooms, however, giant pandas must travel often in order to get enough to eat.

Unlike red pandas, which only eat new bamboo shoots and green leaves, giant pandas consume almost every part of the bamboo plant except the roots. To eat the hard stalk, called "culm," they usually sit upright and grasp the pieces between five fingers and a special enlarged wrist bone that functions as a pseudo-thumb. Pandas then crush the hard-covered fibrous stalk with their powerful jaws and eat the soft, inner tissue. Smaller branches are gnawed in pieces, and leaves are stripped off, wadded up, and swallowed.

Around 12 different varieties of bamboo are grown and harvested at both the San Diego Zoo and Safari Park. The panda keepers at the Zoo serve up—and clean up—big bundles of bamboo for the pandas three times a day. The pandas also eat carrots, yams, and special leaf-eater biscuits packed with vitamins and minerals.

IN THE FIELD

While China's giant pandas require a variety of edible bamboo species to thrive, the bamboo plantations that are taking over much of China's farmland are raising only a few kinds of bamboo as a popular building material—a practice known as "monoculture." When these plantations replace the pandas' habitat, they interrupt the critical food supply that giant pandas need for survival.

GROCERY RUN
The Zoo harvests more than 10 tons of bamboo each year for its giant pandas, red pandas, and takins. Bamboo is one of the world's fastest growing plants.

CHEW ON THIS

Pandas like Mei Sheng eat bamboo almost exclusively; however, this strong grass can wear down their teeth. When pandas cannot properly chew their food, they can't properly digest it. As a result, the Zoo carefully monitors each panda's molars and adjusts their diet as necessary to ensure they get the nutrition they need.

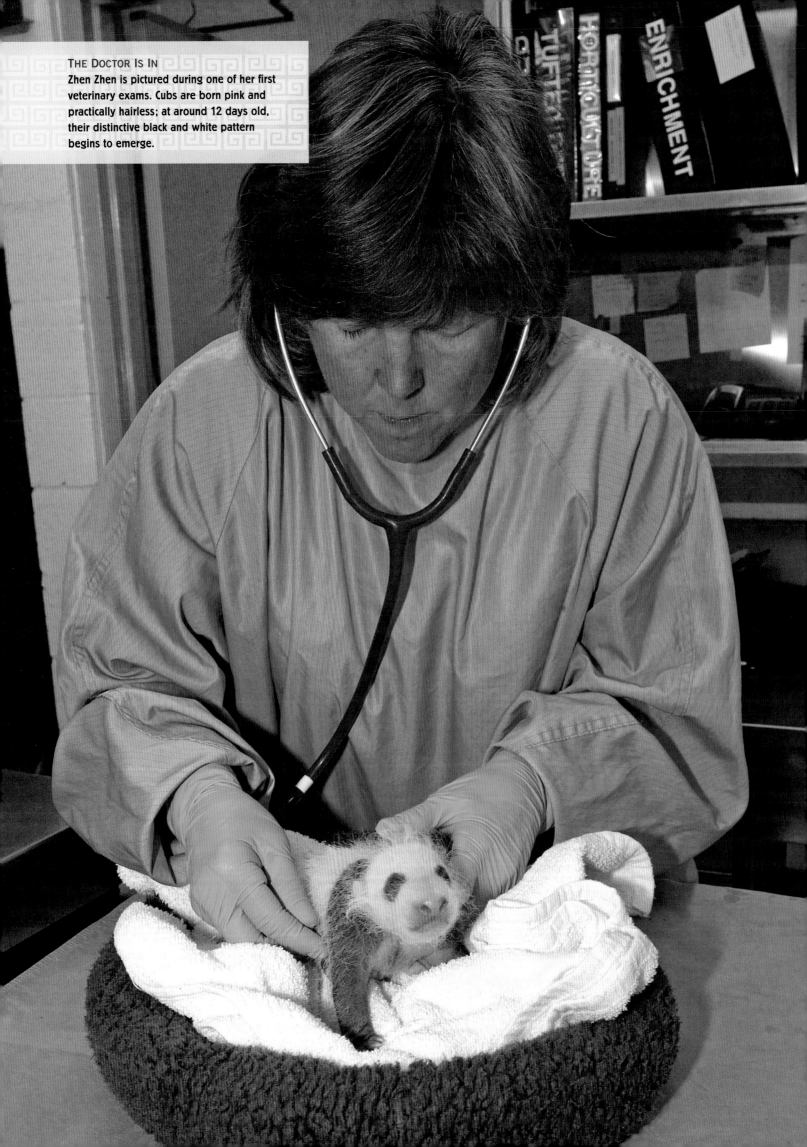

Creature Comforts

The San Diego Zoo's giant pandas are honored guests on loan from China—and like all the animals at the Zoo, these important and popular visitors are provided with the best possible care. Three times a day, they get a specialized, nutritionist-approved bundle of their favorite food, bamboo. The Zoo provides at least three species of bamboo in every bundle, with a mixture of leafy branches and hard, thick stems called culm. Keepers crack open the thickest pieces of culm to lessen the wear on the pandas' teeth. The pandas also get healthy treats like carrots, apples, yams, and vitamin- and mineral-packed leaf-eater biscuits.

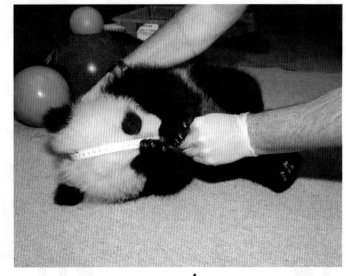

Veterinary care is equally important. Newborn cubs are examined every week until they get too squirmy to handle, and before breeding season, adult pandas are evaluated to ensure they're healthy and ready to mate. (The adults are immobilized for these pre-breeding exams.) To prepare for these medical tests, the pandas are gradually and routinely trained to sit down, place their arm in a metal sleeve for a small blood draw, and open their mouth for inspection and/or medicine. Females are also trained for abdominal ultrasounds so staff can monitor their pregnancies.

CUB CARE
Su Lin, about five months old, has her body measured during a weekly physical exam.

The keepers help the pandas get comfortable with their travel crate as their transport date draws closer. This gradual and positive process involves closing the panda inside his or her crate, making noise in the area, moving the crate (while monitoring the panda's reaction), and giving treats. The goal is to make these activities a normal part of the pandas' routine so they are more comfortable during the long trip to their ancestral home in China.

IN THE FIELD

Giant pandas are considered an "umbrella species." By protecting and caring for pandas, conservationists and panda experts are also caring for an entire range of other species that share the panda's habitat.

PRECIOUS CARGO
An important part of caring for the pandas includes preparing them for their long journey to China. The pandas receive treats and enrichment items inside their crates and are accompanied and carefully monitored by a trusted keeper during the entire process.

Enrichment and Play

Giant pandas in zoos require more than just bamboo to thrive—they also need enrichment that will challenge them mentally, physically, socially, and emotionally. Determining what type of enrichment item each panda will get is no easy task, though. The process involves keepers, nutritionists, veterinarians, construction and maintenance staff, researchers, and sometimes volunteers.

The pandas at the San Diego Zoo receive many types of enrichment. Feeder puzzles, a popular form of enrichment, are made of PVC pipe stuffed with biscuits and fruits. To get the food items to fall out, the pandas must spin the puzzles around and around, trying to stop them in just the right spot. The keepers also place a variety of scents—including cloves, nutmeg, cinnamon, and perfume—on small blocks of wood and put them into the panda enclosures. Bai Yun particularly loves strong perfume and

will rub the scent blocks all over her body.

In addition to daily enrichment, the Zoo creates special events for the pandas every year. For example, on each of the panda's birthdays, the Zoo's Forage Warehouse Staff makes a birthday cake of ice filled with the panda's favorite treats, such as bamboo, yams, or apples. And in the winter, the Zoo creates a "Snow Day," where visitors can see the pandas slipping, sliding, and rolling in the snow.

PUZZLING IT OUT
Like other types of bears, giant pandas are curious, especially when they're young. A suspended ball, such as the one Su Lin is working on at right, is one of the popular puzzles that the pandas use to obtain treats.

SNOW DAY
At times, the San Diego Zoo brings in truckloads of snow for the pandas—such as Hua Mei and Bai Yun, below—to explore, dig, and play in.

HAVING A BALL
Like the other giant pandas, Yun Zi, below right, gets plenty of enrichment to keep him occupied, including tubs of ice, burlap sacks of hay, and hard-plastic containers filled with carrots, yams, apples, and herbivore biscuits.

BIRTHDAY GIRL
Su Lin celebrated her fifth birthday on August 2, 2010, with a special cake made of ice. The Zoo's Forage Warehouse staff freezes favorite food items, such bamboo leaves and slices of yams, inside the cakes.

"It can be very challenging to provide our pandas with the right enrichment. We rotate enrichment items so they remain interesting. Fortunately, our pandas have many fans who donate money toward equipment. This allows us to offer the bears a lot of options."

— Kathy Hawk, *senior keeper*

"We use a number of techniques to assess Bai Yun's estrus status and Gao Gao's interest in her and his motivation to breed. Yard swapping is one of our most informative and simplest techniques. It also primes the bears for what—we hope!—is just around the corner."

— Megan Owen, *conservation program manager*

THE MATING GAME
Breeding may span one or two days, but the actual time that the pandas are together is much less than that. Gao Gao usually lets the Panda Team know when the breeding season is over by not showing interest in Bai Yun anymore.

Getting to Know You

Although they're notoriously solitary, pandas do meet up once in a while, primarily to mate. Giant pandas have a short mating season in the spring. Female pandas communicate that they are ready to mate through a series of body and behavioral changes. For example, their genitalia swell and change color, they scatter chemical signals around their area, and they emit a distinctive chirping sound, rarely at first and then more frequently.

For Bai Yun, who has given birth to six cubs at the Zoo, the timing has generally fallen within a 33-day window from late March to April. Once Bai Yun's scent marking increases and she and Gao Gao—the Zoo's adult male—begin chirping back and forth, the Zoo opens a "howdy gate" so they can see each other. For several days, Bai Yun sends mixed signals to Gao Gao. At times, she acts playful and flirtatious, performing a distinctive backward walk and bleating; at other times, she swats her paw at Gao Gao through the gate and barks to indicate he should stay away. At some point, however, Bai Yun indicates she's truly ready and Gao Gao shows he's clearly interested. Then the Zoo closes the exhibit to the public, brings the pandas together, and gives them their privacy. Over a two to three day period, the pandas may mate several times.

SCENT OF A PANDA
During breeding season, male pandas like Shi Shi get into a handstand position to rub their scent against the trunk of a tree. This advertises their presence to females.

HOWDY, PARTNER
The Zoo uses a "howdy gate" to help Bai Yun and Gao Gao communicate during her fertile time. Once the pandas have demonstrated that they are ready to mate, the keepers open the gate.

Did You Know?

Giant pandas have 13 different vocalizations, including a bleat, chirp, honk, bark, moan, growl, squeal, roar, copulation call, and nursing cry. Most of the time, their bleat is used as a greeting during breeding season to exchange information about sex and age.

Great Expectations

Pandas have a very short mating window, and they only give birth to one or two cubs every other year. So when a panda gets pregnant, it's big news! Panda pregnancies, however, are notoriously hard to predict. Gestation can last as long as 160 days or as little as 101 days due to a process called "embryonic diapause." After mating, a fertilized egg free-floats in the womb for up to four months. Finally, it attaches to the uterine wall, and if all goes well, a baby panda is born 45 to 50 days later.

To make things more complicated, some non-pregnant females—including those who did not mate—can display behavioral and hormonal changes similar to a pregnant female. Even when a panda is pregnant, sometimes an embryo or fetus is miscarried or reabsorbed into the mother's body. The San Diego Zoo has developed a groundbreaking early pregnancy test using thermal imaging and ultrasound. By determining real pregnancy early on, keepers can feed, house, and monitor expectant mothers more appropriately.

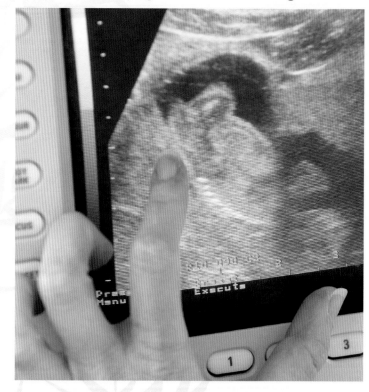

PICTURE THIS
Panda pregnancies are very difficult to confirm. The only way to be certain a giant panda is pregnant is through ultrasound, sometimes just shortly before birth occurs. Su Lin is pictured in her mother's womb at right.

THE DOCTOR IS IN
In addition to ultrasound, the Zoo's animal care staff uses thermography, hormone assays, and behavioral studies to determine a pregnancy.

Did You Know?

For days before and after giving birth, a panda mother will not leave her den for any reason—not even to eat or drink.

A MOTHER'S INSTINCT
Bai Yun has demonstrated superb maternal instincts with each of her six cubs. The Zoo doesn't interfere with Bai Yun's cub rearing and would only step in if the cub or Bai Yun were in distress.

MILESTONE MOMENTS

In 1999, three days before Hua Mei was born, the San Diego Zoo used modern ultrasound technology to see her growing inside her mother's womb and to hear the cub's heartbeat.

"Some of our young cubs quickly learned how to get what they wanted from the keepers. If they didn't want to walk inside at the end of the day, they pretended to be asleep so one of the keepers would carry them inside. Or if they wanted to stay out and didn't want to get picked up, they would get as dirty as possible or try to climb out of our reach."

— Jennifer Beccera, *senior keeper*

Bringing Up Babies

Giant pandas, like all bears, start out small—about the size of a stick of butter! At birth, cubs weigh just three to four ounces and can be gently cradled in their mother's paw. Newborn pandas come out pink, hairless, and completely helpless. Their ears and eyes are closed but their mouths are open, bleating to be fed. At about two weeks, they begin to develop distinctive patches of white and black on their skin. By seven weeks, their eyes are open, and by two months, they've become a cute black and white fur ball that weighs between five and 12 pounds and is just beginning to crawl.

Cubs are up and walking by six months old, able to climb trees and play outside with their mother. At nine months, they begin to chew on bamboo, although they still continue to nurse. Once cubs reach 18 months old, they may weigh as much as 120 pounds and be as big as their mother! It is around this time that mothers begin to prepare for spring breeding by weaning their cubs. The cubs then leave their mothers to live on their own.

LOVE BITES
Su Lin, left, born to Bai Yun in 2005, shares her name with a historic panda. The other Su Lin was the first giant panda to arrive in the United States in 1936.

IN THE FIELD

Female pandas give birth to one or two cubs, which are very dependent on their mothers during their first couple of years of life. In the wild, mother pandas that give birth to twins often focus their care on one cub to ensure its survival. Keepers in China, however, are helping mother pandas raise both cubs through a process called "twin swapping." One baby is left with the mother while keepers care for the other, bottle-feeding it special formula created by a San Diego Zoo nutritionist. Every few days, the keepers switch the twins that so each one gets attention and milk directly from its mother. This practice has increased the survival rate of nursery-reared panda cubs in China from 0 to 95 percent!

WHO'S THAT GIRL?
Born in 2007, Zhen Zhen was a lively cub with an independent streak. Like most panda cubs, Zhen Zhen began climbing when she was about five months old.

AMBASSADOR OF HOPE

The birth of Hua Mei "China USA" in 1999 symbolized the close relationship forged between the United States and China as they work to bring pandas back from the brink of extinction.

NURSING TIME

Bai Yun nurses Zhen Zhen, age four months, below. Panda cubs exclusively nurse until nine months of age, when they begin to eat bamboo. They are weaned from their mothers around 18 months old.

Did You Know?

The average panda "pregnancy" is about 135 days, and the documented range among zoo pandas is 100 to 180 days. However, true gestation of the fetus only takes about 50 days.

PANDA PLAY
Panda cubs love to play, engaging their moms in wrestling, play biting, and chasing. Mei Sheng, above, was born in 2003 to Bai Yun and Gao Gao.

CARRIED AWAY
When panda cubs like Su Lin are young, as pictured above and at right, their mothers carry them around by the scruff of their neck like dogs and cats do. As the cubs get older and bigger, they are allowed to wander a bit more. Bai Yun is patient with all her cubs, but when they displease her, such as by wanting to play while she is eating, she will push them away with her paw or give a soft vocalization.

JUST BORN!

Bai Yun's sixth cub, a boy, was born on July 29, 2012. During his first few exams, keepers noticed that if they put their hand under his chin, he would snuggle up against it.

UP, UP, AND AWAY

As a cub, Su Lin, below and below right, loved to climb—so much so that her keepers began rewarding her with honey, a fruitsicle, or a back scratch if she left her high perch when they called her.

Did You Know?

In accordance with Chinese custom, baby pandas are not named until they are 100 days old.

MILESTONE MOMENTS

In 1987, the Chinese government sent two giant pandas, Basi and Yuan Yuan, to the San Diego Zoo for a 200-day loan. More than two million people viewed the pandas during their stay.

Tracking the Giant Panda

In 1995, when the San Diego Zoo began researching China's giant pandas, there was little information about them. In fact, many in the field feared that giant pandas were doomed to extinction. The Zoo's early trips to China were also much different, involving bushwhacking through miles of dense bamboo forests in search of a munched stem here, a footprint there.

Today, researchers are tracking wild pandas in China's Foping Nature Reserve using radiotelemetry and GPS collars. These small radio collars provide researchers with information on how often and how far wild panda females leave their home range to search for a mate. Their goal is to find out why pandas roam, how they interact with other pandas, and how the fragmented forests affect the panda population. Results may help create natural corridors to link these isolated areas and ensure pandas can move safely through their protected habitat.

Data from the tracking collars also confirm the need for female pandas to have access to warm, dry dens within large, mature trees. This evidence has helped Chinese forestry officials understand the importance of enacting extended logging bans to protect old growth forests. In part because of this information, the Chinese government has increased the number of panda reserves from four to 62 in the last decade, helping to ensure the long-term survival of this beloved species in its native habitat.

A CLOSER LOOK
Pandas are unusually difficult to spot in the wild. Each giant panda requires a large habitat, in some cases up to 100 square miles.

HIGH-TECH TRACKING
By fitting pandas with tracking collars, researchers hope to determine the distance that female pandas travel to find a mate in Foping Preserve.

IN THE FIELD

Fifteen years ago, a pile of droppings found in the field was strong evidence that a giant panda was nearby. Today, applying modern molecular biology, researchers can use fecal samples to study and track a wild panda's specific DNA, diet, overall health, hormones, and reproductive status. In 2010, the Zoo did a study that looked at hormone levels in Gao Gao's fecal material and compared it to his bleat. They found that the longer the sound, the higher his testosterone levels. This study has provided valuable information for researchers who are working to predict breeding cycles.

Conservation and Research

The researchers at the San Diego Zoo Institute for Conservation Research and the Zoo's team of keepers have played an important role in conserving giant pandas. Many of these efforts have been in conjunction with researchers in China—particularly the Wolong Panda Reserve, China's oldest and most respected breeding center. For many years, the Zoo has collaborated with Wolong in nutrition, behavioral enrichment, husbandry, breeding protocols, and verbal and olfactory communications. This research has dramatically increased the giant panda breeding rate at the reserve.

In addition to its research in breeding and births, the San Diego Zoo is conducting a multiyear hearing study that is providing the first glimpse into the giant panda's auditory world. By studying each of the Zoo's pandas in residence, the team hopes to establish what frequencies pandas can hear, whether their hearing sensitivities change during breeding season, and what impact human activities in the wild might have on their hearing. The Zoo hopes this research will lead to measures that will protect the pandas' habitat from harmful activities.

DO YOU HEAR WHAT I HEAR?
Since 2009, the San Diego Zoo has been studying the hearing range of giant pandas to determine what noises might disturb them or disrupt important communication in their natural habitat.

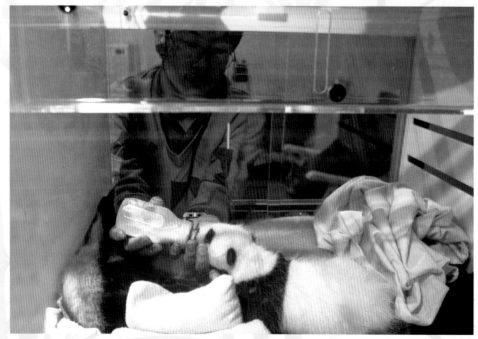

WOLONG NURSERY
More than 66 cubs have been born at Wolong Preserve. Bai Yun herself was born at Wolong in 1991, marking the first successful birth of a giant panda at the center.

"At the Zoo, we've been involved in a number of research studies on pandas' communication, from secret signals to vocalizations. We're also studying the hearing range of giant pandas. This research is enabling us to better assess how human-generated noise might disturb giant pandas or disrupt important communication."

— Megan Owen, *conservation program manager*

MILESTONE MOMENTS

In 2010, the panda population in zoos and breeding centers reached 300. This goal was set years ago by international scientists and is believed to be the point at which the captive population can be self-sustaining. With 300 pandas living in managed care, the population has a genetic buffer against the difficulties giant pandas are facing in the wild.

A LITTLE LEARNER
Yun Zi, shown at right as a young cub, has been participating in the Zoo's landmark hearing study since 2012. Data points are recorded when the bears show they can hear a tone during a study session.

MEASURING UP
Yun Zi, pictured below with his eyes still closed at about six weeks old, has a routine veterinary exam. Pandas will open their eyes when they are between 50 and 60 days old.

PANDA PARTNERS
The San Diego Zoo is working with colleagues at the Wolong Panda Preserve as they prepare for a large-scale reintroduction program that involves releasing captive-born pandas into a protected habitat.

TRAINING DAY
Panda keepers Kathy Hawk (left) and JoAnne Simerson work with four-month-old Zhen Zhen. The Zoo works with each cub early on to establish a rapport that will make routine care easier later on.

GLOBAL RESEARCH
Through captive propagation programs in China, the San Diego Zoo, and other zoos around the world, the Zoo is learning more about the care of panda cubs and how to help them reach adulthood.

IN THE FIELD

About a month before giving birth, a pregnant panda will seek out and prepare a warm, dry den, lining it with soft shreds of bamboo. Zoo researchers are studying these maternity dens in the field. They hope to determine why a panda chooses a den, the extent to which the logging of old-growth trees in China has eliminated many high-quality dens, and how artificial dens might serve wild pandas in areas where natural dens have been destroyed.

MONKEY BUSINESS
The first animals the San Diego Zoo received on loan from China were a pair of Sichuan golden monkeys from 1984 to 1985. These monkeys are endangered due to habitat loss.

The 100-acre San Diego Zoo is dedicated to the conservation of endangered species and their habitats. The organization focuses on conservation and research work around the globe, educates millions of individuals a year about wildlife, and maintains accredited horticultural, animal, library, and photo collections. The Zoo also manages the 1,800-acre San Diego Zoo Safari Park (historically referred to as the Wild Animal Park), which includes an 800-acre native species reserve, and the San Diego Zoo Institute for Conservation Research. The important conservation and science work of these entities is supported in part by the Foundation of the Zoological Society of San Diego.

ISBN: 978-1-935442-18-9
Printed in the United States of America
10 9 8 7 6 5 4 3 2 1

Panda Trek was developed by Beckon Books in cooperation with the San Diego Zoo. Beckon develops and publishes custom books for leading cultural attractions, corporations, and non-profit organizations. Beckon Books is an imprint of Southwestern Publishing Group, Inc., 2451 Atrium Way, Nashville, TN 37214. Southwestern Publishing Group, Inc., is a wholly owned subsidiary of Southwestern, Inc., Nashville, Tennessee.

Christopher G. Capen, *President, Beckon Books*
Monika Stout, *Design/Production*
Betsy Holt, *Writer/Editor*
www.beckonbooks.com
877-311-0155

An International Effort

Four decades ago, when the San Diego Zoo's relationship with China had just begun, giant pandas faced possible extinction. Today, giant pandas face a much more promising future, in part because the Chinese government has developed a conservation strategy, established more than 60 panda reserves, and permitted unprecedented research studies and collaborations among national and international scientists.

The San Diego Zoo's collaboration with China began in 1973, when Clayton Swanson, then the general manager of the Zoo, visited a series of Chinese zoos. Eventually, these trips led to the Zoo hosting a pair of rare golden monkeys from 1984 to 1985. That year, the Zoo also signed an historic 10-year agreement with the China Wildlife Conservation Association in Beijing, which promoted cooperative research efforts for various endangered species in China.

In 1996, after an extensive documentation and permitting process, the Zoo welcomed giant pandas Bai Yun and Shi Shi for a 12-year breeding and research loan, which has since been renewed. Their first cub, Hua Mei, was born in 1999, and five more cubs were sired by another male, Gao Gao, who arrived on loan in 2003. The San Diego Zoo and its Chinese colleagues are continuing to address the changing needs of giant pandas—recognizing that conservation of a species and its habitat is a lifetime endeavor.

ZOO FIRSTS
The first giant pandas the Zoo received on loan from China were Bai Yun and Shi Shi (pictured). The Zoo put them together when the mating window was open, but Shi Shi, who was older, was more interested in eating bamboo.

MILESTONE MOMENTS

In 1984, China began to offer pandas to other nations as part of a 10-year loan program for up to $1 million dollars per year. Under U.S. law, more than half the loan fees must be channeled into conservation efforts for China's wild pandas and their habitats. Today, four American zoos host pandas: the San Diego Zoo, the National Zoo in Washington, D.C., Zoo Atlanta, and the Memphis Zoo.

HER OWN LEGACY
Hua Mei (pictured with mom Bai Yun) went to live at Wolong Panda Breeding Center in 2004. Hua Mei has since given birth to nine cubs of her own, including three sets of twins.